Karin Groß

21 Charakterstücke-Leicht bis mittelschwer in beiden Instrumenten

21 Character Pieces-easy to moderately difficult for both instruments

Illustrationen /Illustrations: Wolfgang Steinmeyer

VORWORT

Spielfreude ist auch das Motto des zweiten Bandes dieser Duo-Sammlung. 21 leicht erfassbare Charakterstücke beschreiben unterschiedlichste Stimmungen und Szenarien: Wasserspiele glitzern, Herbstfarben leuchten, wilde Hühner sorgen für Aufregung, ein entspannter Einkaufsbummel steht ebenso auf dem Programm wie eine melancholische Reise in den Orient ...

Mein Ziel war es, ansprechende Stücke zu schreiben, die in beiden Instrumenten einen ähnlichen Schwierigkeitsgrad aufweisen, so dass sie von Gleichaltrigen gespielt werden können.

Im Mittelpunkt steht das Zusammenspiel: aufeinander hören, im Hintergrund bleiben oder in den Vordergrund treten. Beide Instrumente haben sowohl solistische als auch begleitende Aufgaben. Die Geigenstimme ist in der ersten Lage spielbar. Alle Stücke sind mit Fingersätzen bzw. Strichvorschlägen versehen.

Mein ganz herzlicher Dank gilt Annette Demond (Cello) und Bernd-Udo Winker (Geige und Bratsche) für ihre fachliche Beratung in Streicherfragen!

Karin Groß, Dortmund 2019

PREFACE

The joys of playing remains the motto of the second volume of this collection of duos too. 21 easily accessible character pieces conjure up a wide variety of moods and settings: water displays sparkle, autumnal colours glow, wild chickens cause quite a commotion, and there is both a relaxed shopping trip in store as well as a melancholy journey to the Orient ...

It was my aim to write enchanting pieces which are similar in their level of difficulty for both instruments so that they can be played by musicians of the same age.

The focus is on playing together: listening to each other, staying in the background or coming to the fore. Both instruments take solo as well as accompanying roles. The violin part can be played in the first position. Fingerings and suggestions for bowings are included for all the pieces.

I am extremely grateful to Annette Demond (cello) and Bernd-Udo Winker (violin and viola) for the expert advice they gave me concerning their instruments.

Karin Groß, Dortmund 2019

Impressum

VHR 3437 / ISMN 979-0-2013-1015-2 / ISBN 978-3-86434-112-0

Notensatz: Karin Groß, Dortmund

Illustrationen: Wolfgang Steinmeyer, Waltenhofen
Umschlaggestaltung: Gerhard Illig Kommunikation, Erlangen
Foto: Peter Leßmann, Münster

www.holzschuh-verlag.de

INHALT CONTENTS

Schwere Jungs

Big-time Crooks

Karin Groß

Wasserspiele
Water Displays

Animato

Karin Groß

13

17
mf
8va
mf
8va

21
pizz.
p
8va
l.H.
p

Herbstfarben
Autumnal Colours

Karin Groß

13
2
1
5
3
2

17
2
1
5
1
5

21
2
5
1
3
1
2
1

Schuhputz-Song
Cleaning Shoes Song

Lebhaft
Lively

Karin Groß

10
4
1
5
2
5

14
4
1
4
3
2
3
2
1
2

18
5
2
4
1
5
2
1
2

Zwiefacher

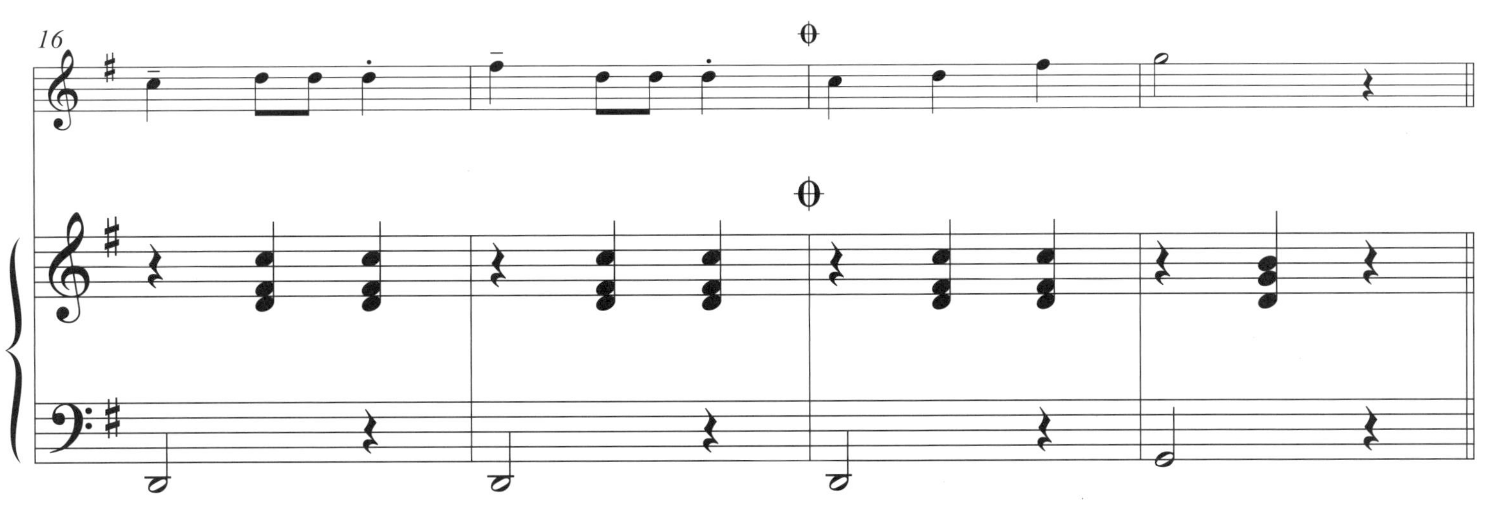
16

20
mf
f
1 3 5
1 2
5

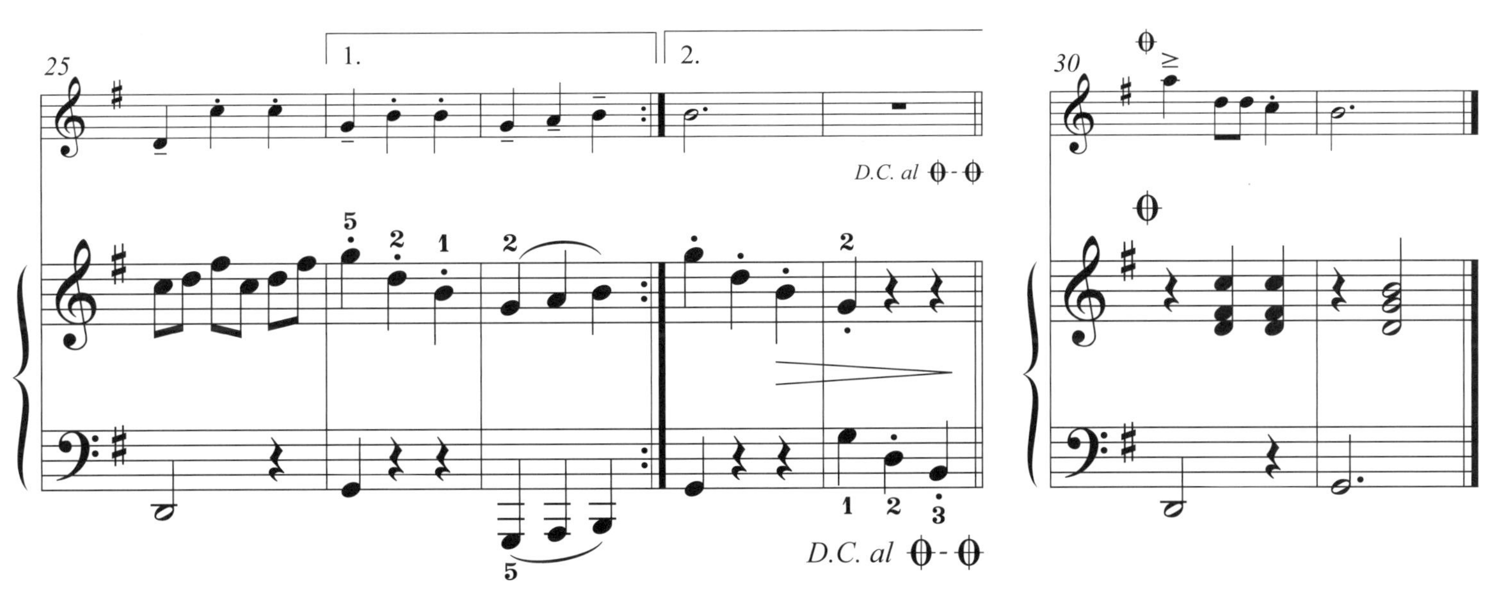
25
1.
2.
D.C. al 𝄌 - 𝄌
5 2 1
2
2
5
1 2 3
D.C. al 𝄌 - 𝄌
30

Am Kamin

By The Fireside

Friedlich
Peacefully

Karin Groß

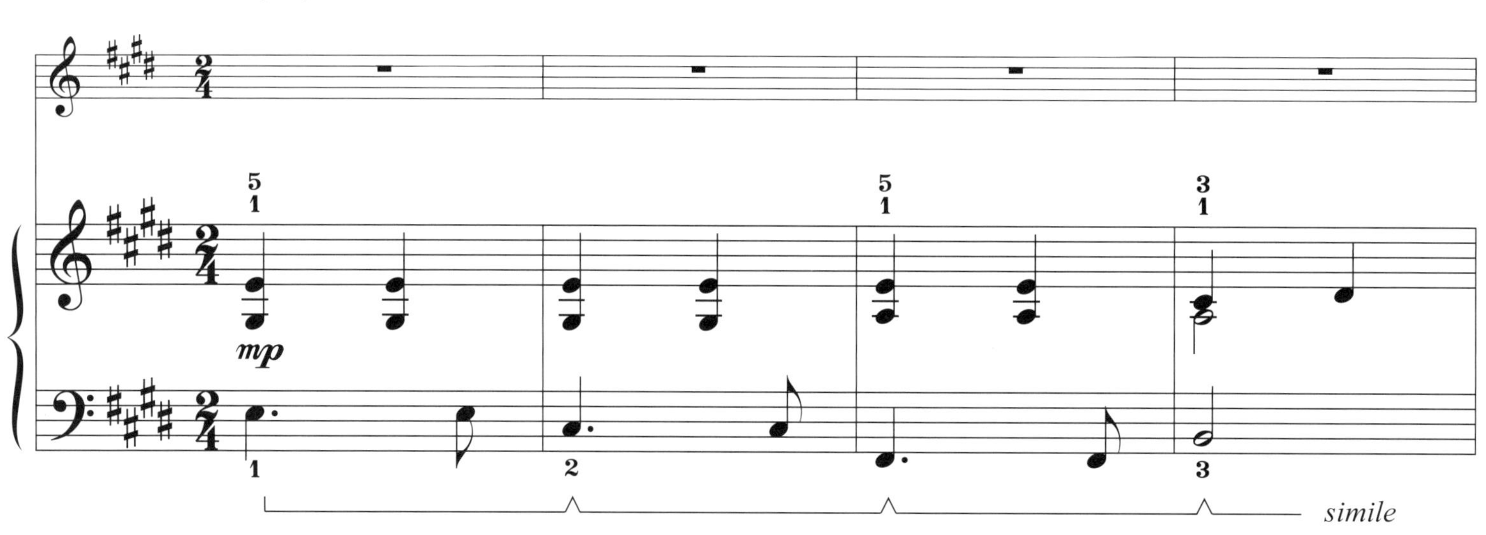

13
mf
5
2
mf

17
2

21
mp
rit.

Aufregung im Hühnerhof

Mit Humor
With humour

Karin Groß

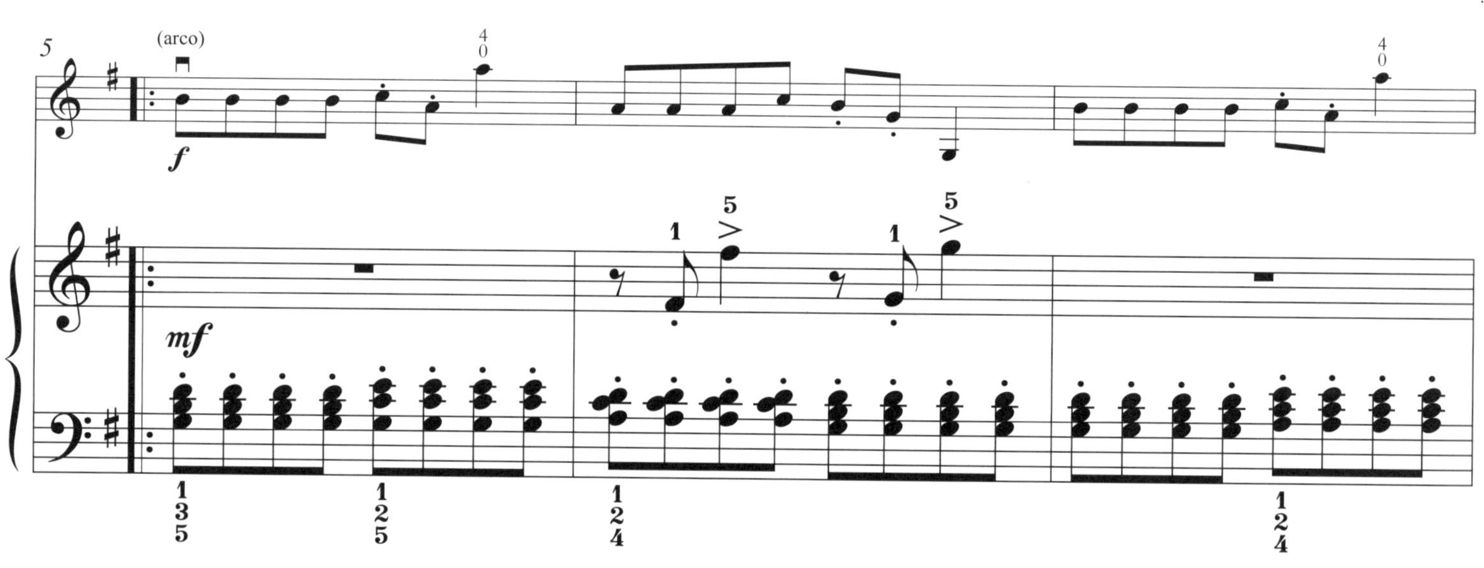

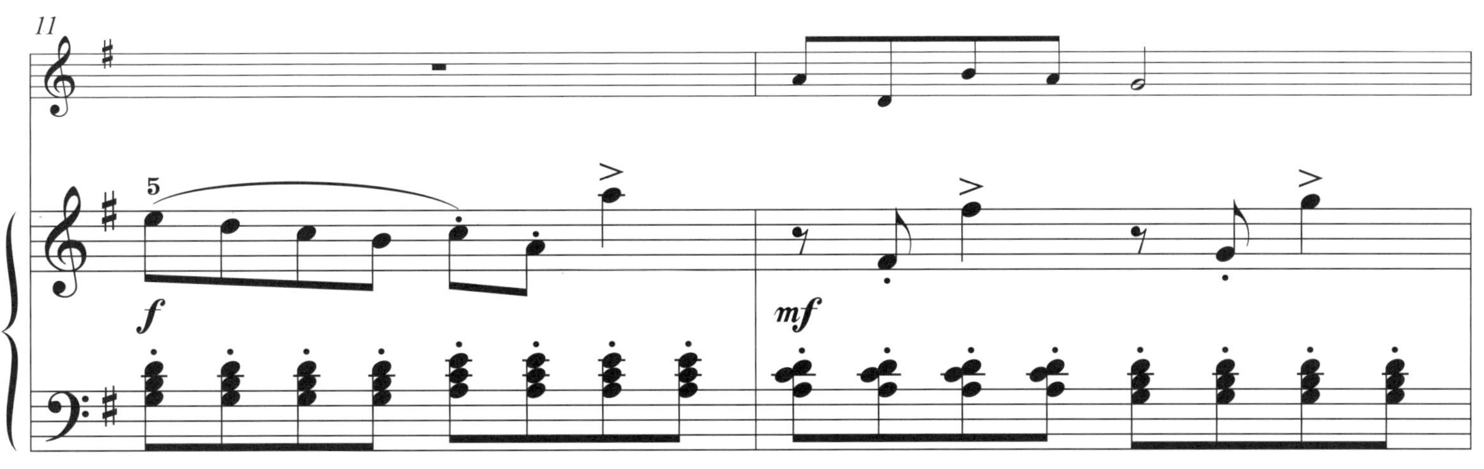
11
5
f
mf

13
pizz.
mf
1.
3
1
p
4

17
2.
arco
4
0
f
mf

Jacques' Akkordeon
Jacques' Accordion

17
f
mf
21
25
mf
simile
29
f
f

Paarlauf

Pair Skating

Allegro

Karin Groß

13

17
mf
mf

21
f
f

Aus längst vergessener Zeit

From Long-forgotten Times

Moderato

Karin Groß

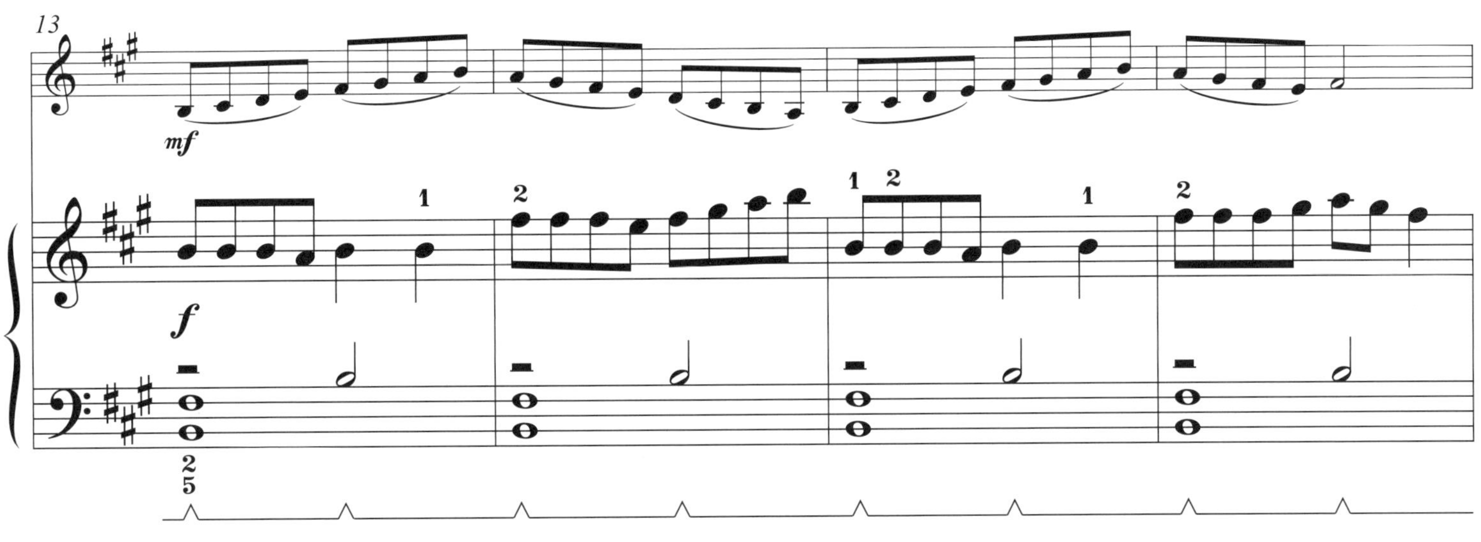
13
mf
f

17
f
mf

21
dim.
rit.
p
dim.
rit.

Siciliano

Karin Groß

Geige

Violin

INHALT CONTENTS

Schwere Jungs
Big-time Crooks

Karin Groß

Wasserspiele
Water Displays

Animato

Karin Groß

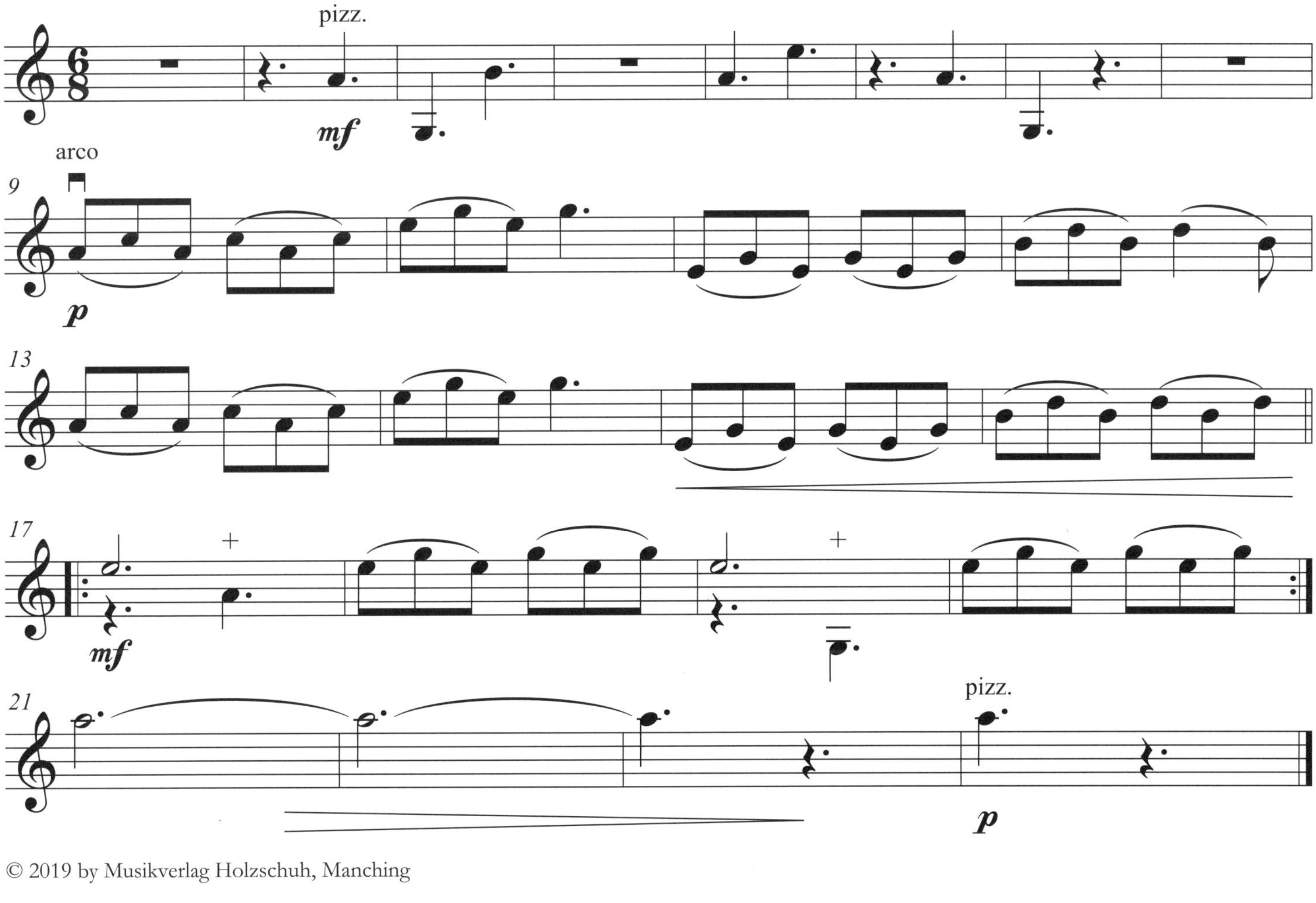

pizz.

mf

arco

9

p

13

17

mf

21

pizz.

p

Herbstfarben

Autumnal Colours

Karin Groß

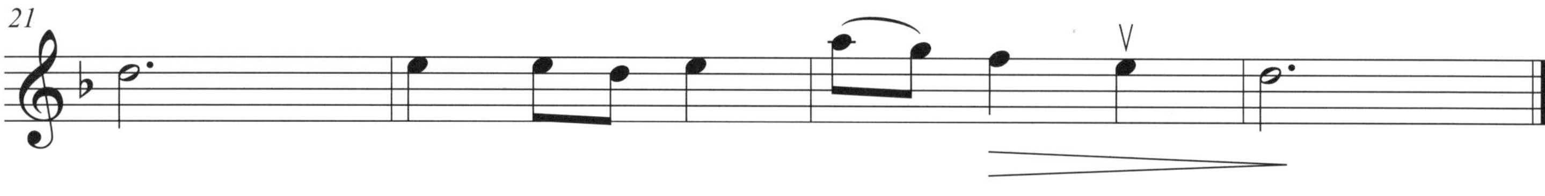

Schuhputz-Song

Cleaning Shoes Song

Zwiefacher

Schwungvoll
Full of vigour

Karin Groß

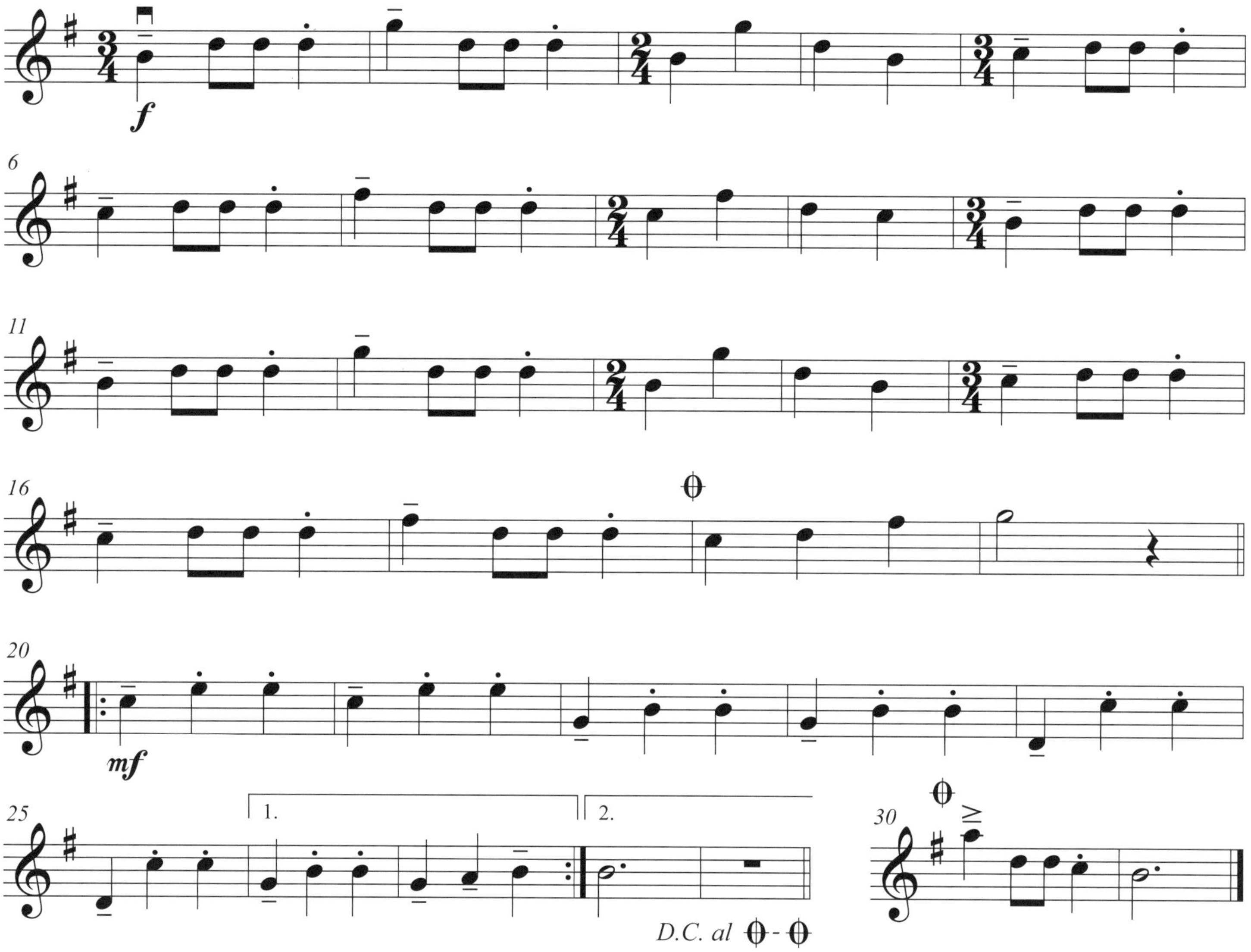

f

6

11

16

20

mf

25

1.

2.

D.C. al 𝄌 - 𝄌

30

Am Kamin

By The Fireside

Friedlich
Peacefully

Karin Groß

Aufregung im Hühnerhof

Commotion In The Chicken Run

Mit Humor
With humour

Karin Groß

(arco)

pizz.

1.

2.

arco

Jacques' Akkordeon
Jacques' Accordion

Beschwingt
Buoyantly

Karin Groß

Paarlauf
Pair Skating

Karin Groß

Aus längst vergessener Zeit

From Long-forgotten Times

Moderato

Karin Groß

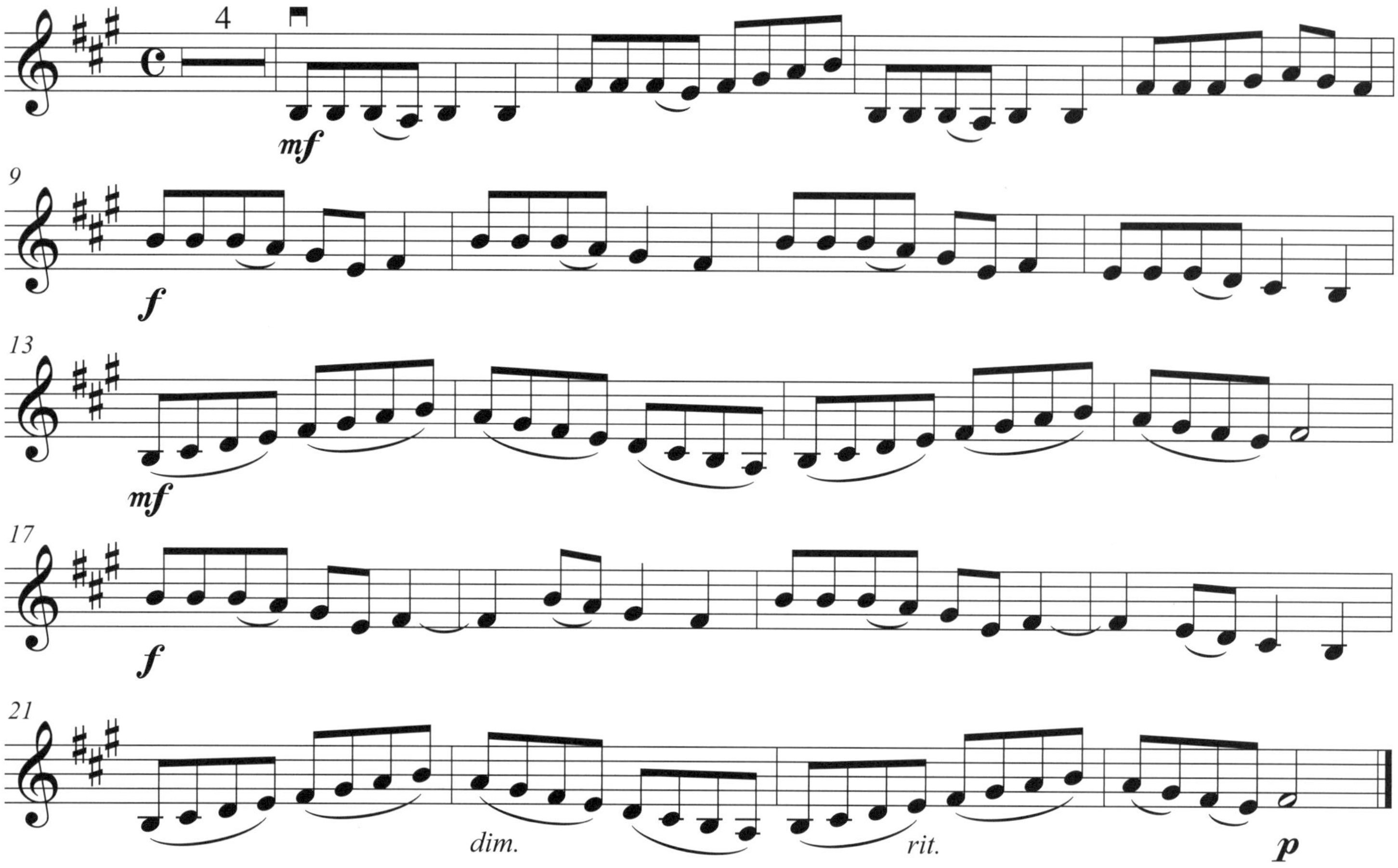
4
mf
9
f
13
mf
17
f
21
dim.
rit.
p

Siciliano

Feierlich
Festively

Karin Groß

2
mf
7
1.
11
2.
rit.

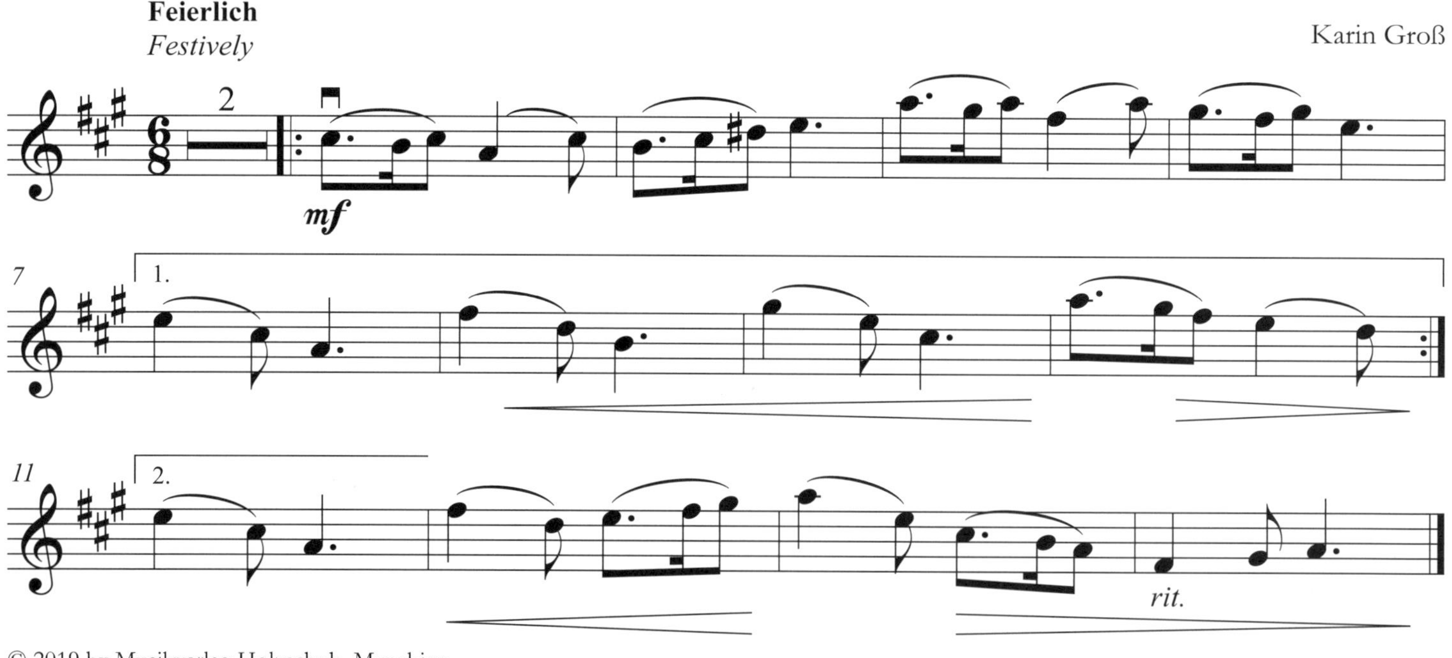

Pfannekuchen-Rag

Pancake Rag

Einkaufsbummel

A Shopping Trip

Menuett

Minuet

Karin Groß

Dringende Bitte

An Urgent Appeal

Leidenschaftlich
Passionately

Karin Groß

Thema mit Variationen

Theme With Variations

Karin Groß

Variation 1
14
pizz.
mf
1.
2.
19
arco
4
0
4
0
4
0
4
0
pizz.
p
mf
Variation 2
arco
27
mp
31
mf
35
p
39
mp
Variation 3
43
mf
47
51
p

55
mf
Variation 4 Minore
59
mf
63
p
67
mf
Variation 5 Maggiore
71
mf
1.
2.
76
p
cresc.
80
f
84
mf
88
cresc.
ff
rit.

Tarantella

Karin Groß

Haken schlagen
Darting Sideways

Sportlich
Sportily

Karin Groß

Fünfer
A Fiver

Orientalisches Lied

Oriental Song

Karin Groß

Abschiedswalzer

Farewell Waltz

Karin Groß

4

mf

9

13

mf

18

1.

2.

23

mf

27

31

35

molto rit.

Pancake Rag

Gut gelaunt
In a good mood

Karin Groß

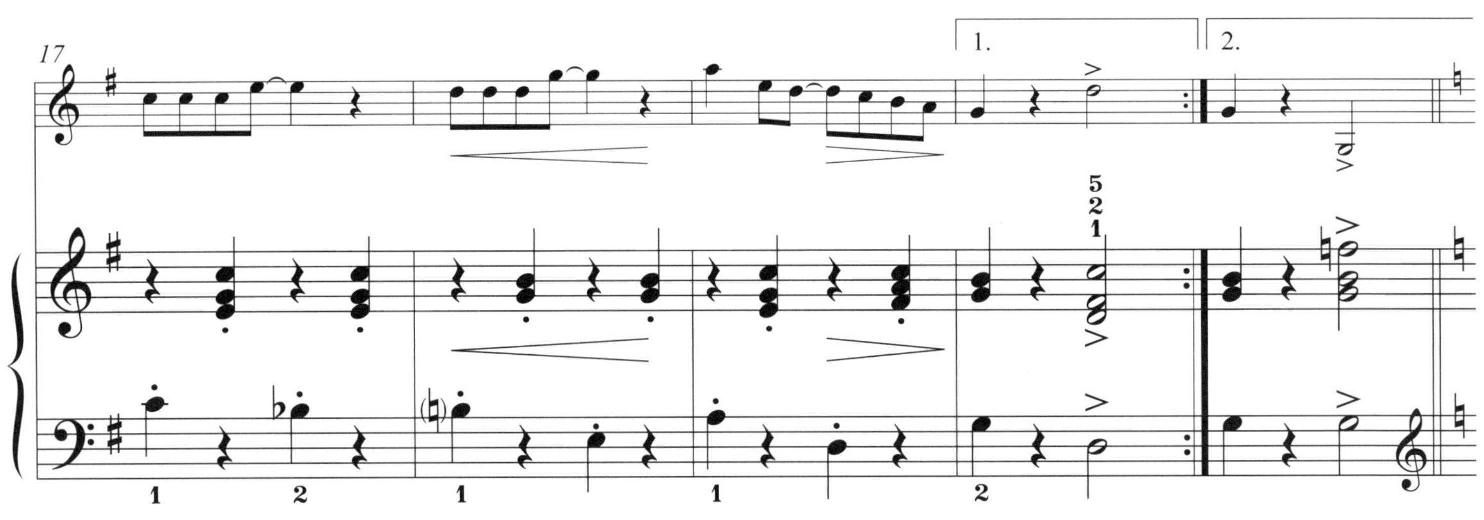

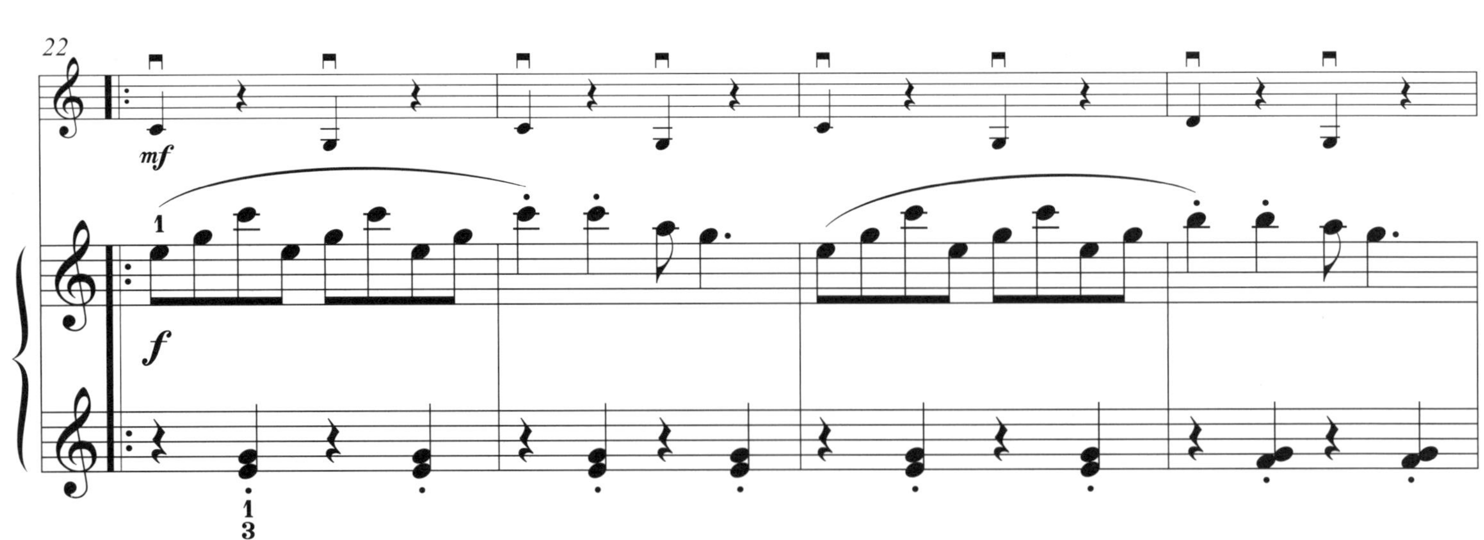

26
1.
f
3

30
2.
f
D.S. al 𝄌 - 𝄌
senza rep.
D.S. al 𝄌 - 𝄌
senza rep.

33

Einkaufsbummel

A Shopping Trip

Karin Groß

Menuett

Minuet

Karin Groß

Dringende Bitte

An Urgent Appeal

15
mf
mp
3 2
1 4
1 3
2 4

19
p
mf

23
1.
2.
mf
rit.
p
rit.

Thema mit Variationen

Theme With Variations

Karin Groß

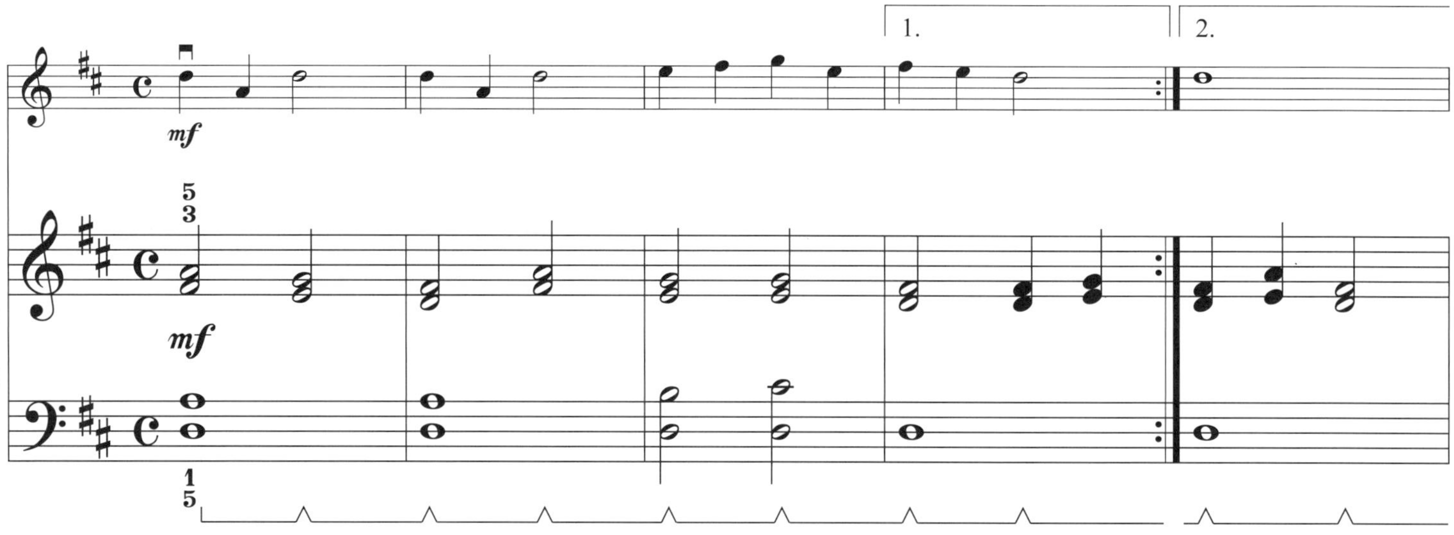

1. 2.

mf

mf

Variation 1

19
arco
4
0
mf
p
3
1
5
3
4
2
5
3

23
pizz.
mf
5
5

Variation 2

27
arco
mp
2
4
1
3
1
4
1
simile

31
mf
2
1
5
1
1

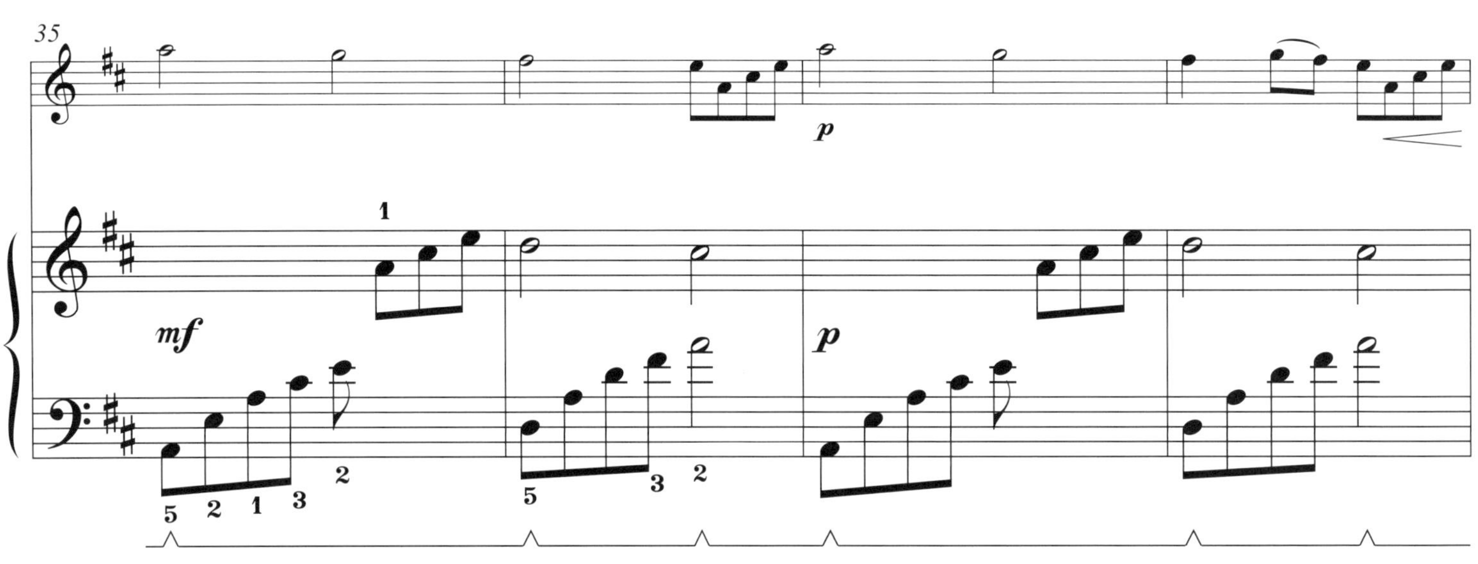
35
p
1
mf
p
5
2
1
3
2
5
3
2

39
mp
mp

Variation 3

43
mf
47
51
p
55
mf
Variation 4 Minore
59
mf
5
3
4
5
4
63
p
1
2
1
3
3
1
2
1
3
3
4

Variation 5 *Maggiore*

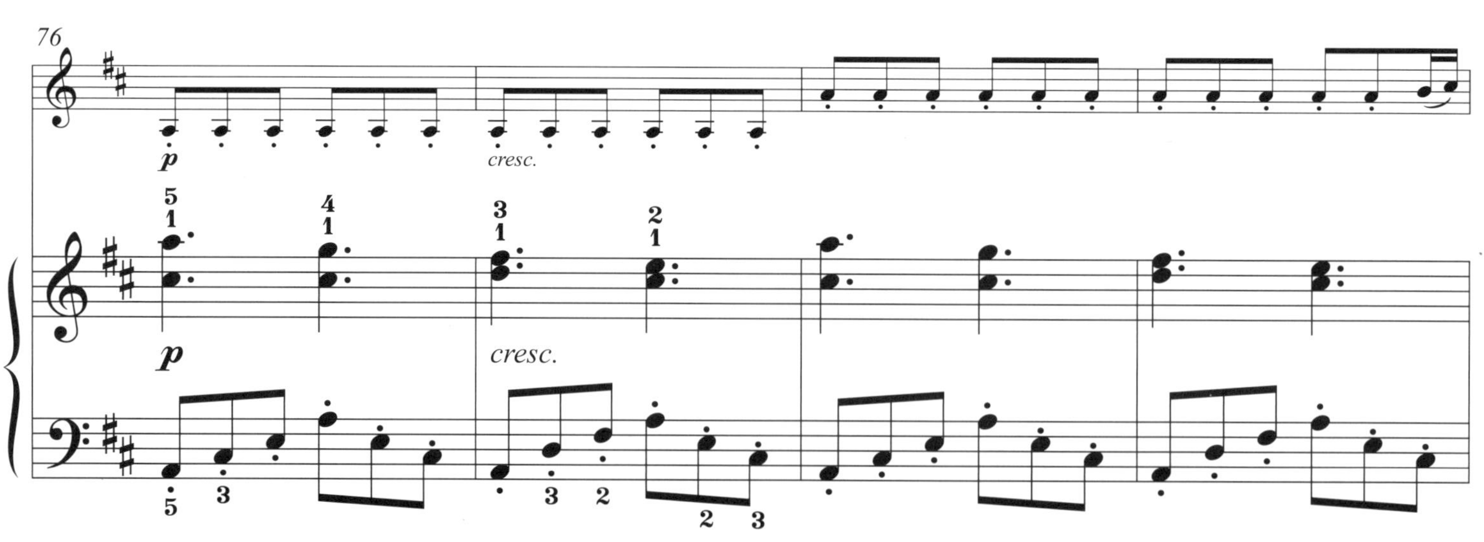

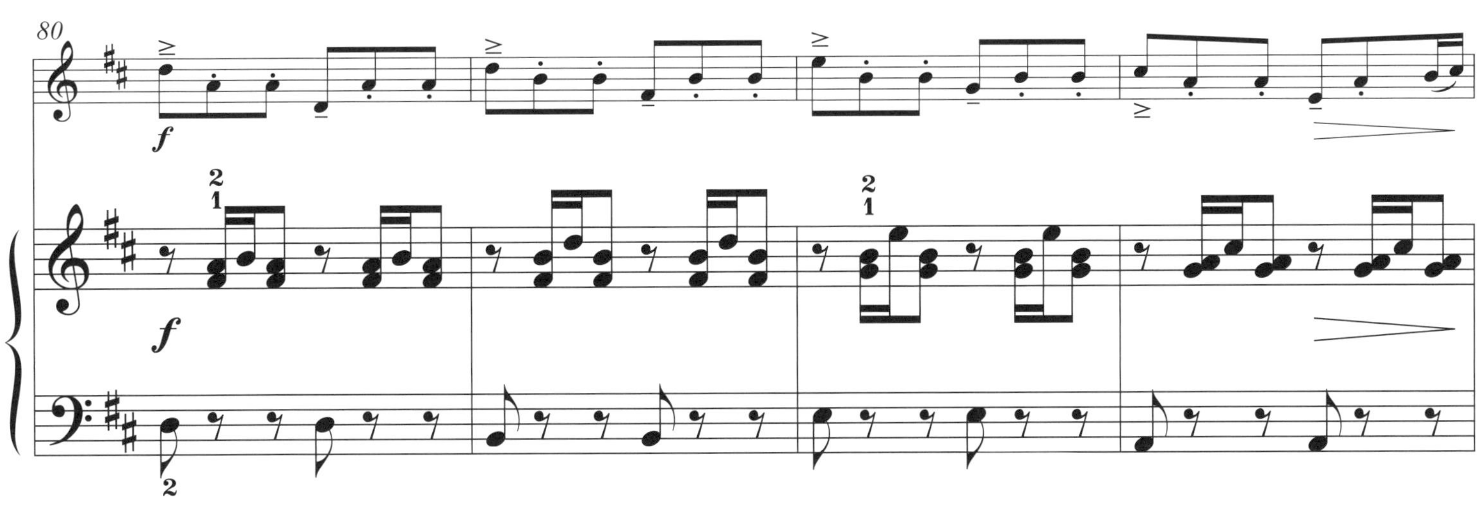
80
f
f

84
mf
mf

88
cresc.
ff
rit.
cresc.
ff
rit.

Tarantella

Temperamentvoll
Spiritedly

Karin Groß

mf
mf
p
p
mf
cresc.
cresc.
f
f
D.S. al Fine
senza rep.
D.S. al Fine
senza rep.

Haken schlagen
Darting Sideways

Sportlich
Sportily

Karin Groß

15
f

19
f
mf

23
p
mf

Fünfer

A Fiver

Vivo

Karin Groß

mf 4 1 3 p 3 1 3 7 3 11 mf 2 f 1 2 1

15
f
mf
19
23
27
mf
p
f
mf

Orientalisches Lied

Oriental Song

Doloroso

Karin Groß

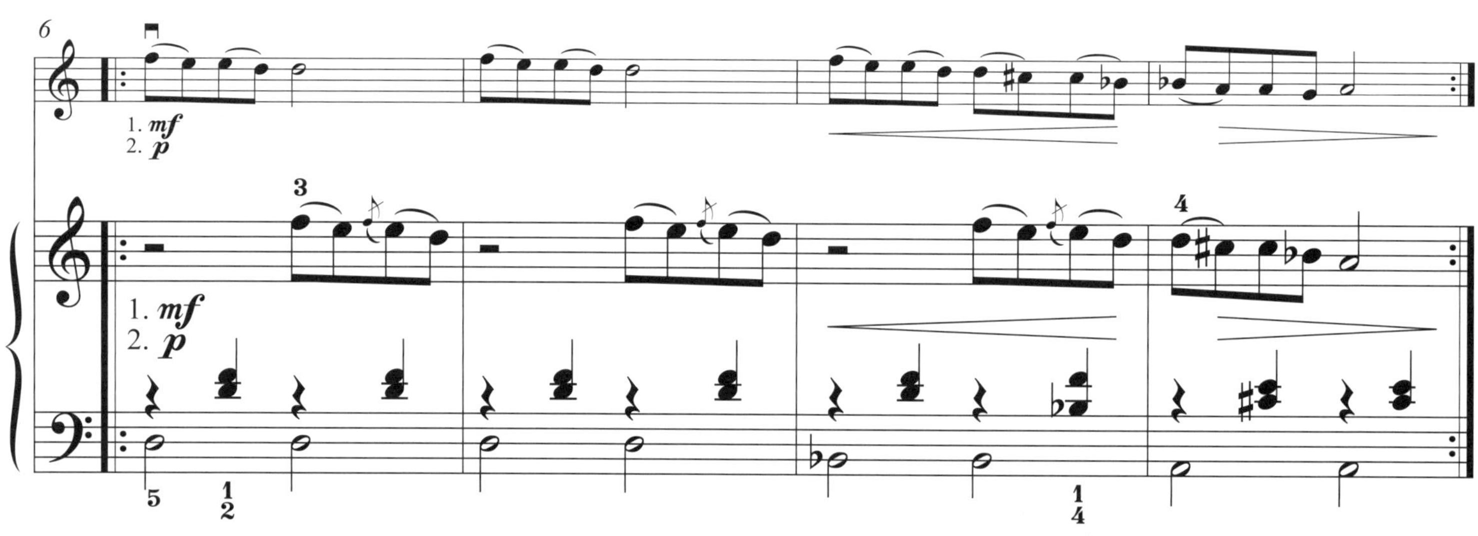

15
pizz.
mf

arco
19
mf

23
p
molto rit.
p
molto rit.

Abschiedswalzer

Farewell Waltz

Karin Groß

13
mf
mf

18
1.
2.

23
mf
p

27
3
mf
4
3
4

31
3
1
p
3

35
molto rit.
molto rit.